Ashtavakra

❧ The Vedic Sage ☙

Ashtavakra
❧ The Vedic Sage ☙

*Unusual Tales of the Country called
"Bharat"*

by

Gopish Gopalkrishna

www.whitefalconpublishing.com

Ashtavakra - The Vedic Sage
Gopish Gopalkrishna

www.whitefalconpublishing.com

The contents of this book have been timestamped on the
Ethereum blockchain as a permanent proof of existence.
Scan the QR code or visit the URL given on the back
cover to verify the blockchain certification for this book.

Requests for permission should be addressed to
gopishtheblogger@gmail.com

ISBN - 978-93-89530-88-9

Dedicated to

My Father Gopalkrishna Pillai, Mother Syamala Pillai,
Wife Greeshma, Children Giaa and Gyansh
Brother Girish, Sister-in-law Kala, Nieces Vibhuti and Vedika
and
Dear Sudha Murthy

CONTENTS

ACKNOWLEDGEMENT

I started reading books in 2007, and my first book was "One night at the Call Center" written by Chetan Bhagat. This was the start of my reading journey which is still continuing. I am inspired by Chetan Bhagat and Sudha Murthy's works. They and their writings are my inspiration to write this book. This book "Ashtavakra - The Vedic Sage" is dedicated to Sudha Murthy who is one of my favourite authors. All her books, especially "The Serpent's Revenge", "The Man from Egg", "The Upside-down King", etc. have inspired me a lot.

The world is a better place with supportive family members, great colleagues, and friends; I am blessed to have them around. Without their encouragement and support, writing a book would have been difficult.

I am everlastingly grateful to my parents, **Mr. Gopalkrishna Pillai** and **Mrs. Syamala Pillai** for their love, care, and freedom to do whatever I wanted in my life.

I would like to thank my wife, **Greeshma,** who helped me with reading early drafts, and also motivating me to publish my first book.

Thanks to my inspiration and the purpose of my life - **Giaa** and **Gyansh,** my lovely kids and precious gifts from the Almighty.

All sketch credits go to **Nabanita,** an amazing artist who can be reached at nabanita81.official@gmail.com.

Special thanks to everyone from the White Falcon Publishing team.

Last but not least, to all my readers who bought this book to read.

DISCLAIMER

This is a work of fiction, written with the only intention of entertaining book lovers and readers. All situations and characters, with the exception of some well-known mythological figures in this novel, are products of the author's imagination and are not to be construed as real. While the content has several references to places, names, persons, ancient events, religions, beliefs, and myths, it is all written with the purpose of making a fictional story richer and fascinating. The author is a believer in all faiths and religions and respects them equally. The author makes no claim to the correctness and authenticity of any historical or mythological or contextual references used in the book.

1

THE COUNTRY: BHARAT

During 2700 BC, there lived King Sudas who ruled the Bharata Kingdom. King Sudas was the son of King Paijavana and grandson of King Divodas Atithigva. His empire spanned the regions of Punjab near Sarasvati River. The Purus were a coalition of tribes settled at the banks of the River Sarasvati. The Bharatas are descendants of the Purus and King Sudas was the descendant of the Emperor of Bharata.

Great Sage Vishwamitra was the high priest in King Sudas' Kingdom. Under his guidance, Sudas won many battles and kingdoms. One day due to some misunderstanding, Vishwamitra was sacked by Sudas. Sage Vashistha was appointed as the new priest, and Vishwamitra was asked to leave the kingdom immediately. Vishwamitra felt humiliated. Post this, there was a long rivalry between Vashistha and Vishwamitra. Eventually, Vishwamitra decided to fight Sudas. He created an alliance with the powerful Puru tribes and other tribes from Persia and nearby regions to attack Sudas. A total of ten tribes came together and created an alliance against Sudas.

The battle took place on the banks of Parusni (Ravi) River which lasted for many years. Sudas and his army fought bravely with all the tribe forces and managed to cross Parusni River. Sudas was able to defeat the alliance of the ten-tribe kings and emerged victorious. This war is famously known as the Dasharajanya war; this was one of its kind organized war where infantry, elephants and archers were used to fight in the battle.

After this war, many inhabitants of the region moved out and migrated to Iran and nearby areas. However, many Western scholars misconstrued this battle as an invasion on Aryans, but it was a war between Aryans in which the superior Aryan kings with spiritual values won and established their kingdom.

By the time this war got over, the Bharatas, who are believed to be Vedic Hindus, occupied a vast territory, from the banks of Jamuna to Iran in the West. In current geographic terms, it covers the entire North India, Pakistan, Afghanistan, and Iran. When Sudas conquered the entire region, it came to be known as "Bharata" which is currently known as India. Sudas, Bharata ruler, later allied and merged with the Purus and formed the Kuru dynasty. Kauravas and Pandavas were the 15th generation of the Kuru dynasty who fought the epic war "Mahabharata".

2

YUDHISTHIRA'S CURSE ON WOMANHOOD

The Mahabharata war lasted for 18 days; this war corrupted almost all warriors who fought it. Every warrior resorted to deception and treachery. When this biggest war was over, only Pandavas and a few handful of others survived. However, their lives changed after the war. Even though the war was over, Pandavas continued to stay on the banks of Ganga to perform the last rites of all the people who died in Kurukshetra's war. Yudhisthira was deeply hurt as he lost many of his army men and relatives. He was grief-stricken and felt that his own greed had led to the loss of life of the warriors and relatives.

None of the Pandavas, including Yudhisthira, knew that Karna was their elder brother. Karna was born to Kunti (mother of Pandavas) with the blessings of Lord Surya. At that time, Kunti was unmarried. Fearing embarrassment and dishonor, Kunti decided to abandon her child. She put the baby in a basket and set it afloat the mighty Ganga. Kunti was later married to Pandu, the King of Hastinapur and gave birth to Pandavas. Kunti kept this secret till the Mahabharata war was over and Karna was killed.

After Karna's death, when Kunti revealed this secret; Yudhisthira and other Pandavas were very upset and angry. Yudhisthira was very depressed and had tears in his eyes; he could not control his emotions.

Kunti came forward and explained, "Hey Yudhisthira, please don't cry. I had informed Karna about his relationship with Pandavas and me. I also tried to convince Karna to give up his enmity against Pandavas. However, Karna didn't agree due to his intimate friendship with Duryodhana. I tried a lot to change his mind but eventually gave up on Karna's decision to fight the war along with Duryodhana," she finished and cried irrepressibly.

When King Yudhisthira heard his mother Kunti's words of solace, he was very upset that his mother had kept an enormous secret from him and the others. He could not contain his anger and cursed that henceforward entire womanhood would not be able to hide any secrets.

It is said that due to this curse of King Yudhisthira, no woman can keep a secret, no matter how personal or confidential the information is.

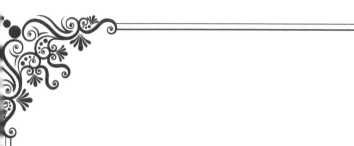

3

SITA AND HER FIVE WITNESSES

Whenever we hear of Devi Sita, the one thing which strikes us is her absolute love and faith towards Lord Rama. Devi Sita signifies the meaning of an ideal woman, who is faithful to her husband Rama. One does not associate Devi Sita with curses. She was modest and didn't believe in putting herself forward unless there is a necessity. But she was not a silent sufferer. She had a clear idea of self-worth, but this did not lead her to downsize the worth of others. At decisive times, she made her voice heard, loud and clear. Coming to the curses, Devi Sita herself had one story.

This incident happened when Lord Rama, Devi Sita and Lakshman were in exile. During this period, King Dasharatha, father of Lord Rama, died as he was not able to bear the pain of separation of his children. When Rama and Lakshman got the news of their father's death, they decided to perform the *shraad* or *pind-daan* (a Hindu ritual where offerings are given to the departed souls).

Shraad is performed in the remembrance of the deceased relative, according to the *Panchang* (Hindu calendar) or *Pitra Paksha*. As per Hindu rituals, *Pitra Paksha* is considered the best time to pay gratitude to the ancestors. So, day and time were decided by Lord Rama and Lakshman to perform the *shraad* for their father, Dasharatha. During this phase of exile, they were in a city called Gaya, in Bihar; they decided to perform the rituals at the bank of Phalgu River.

On the day of *pind-daan* early morning, all three of them reached at the bank of Phalgu River. Both Lord Rama and Lakshman went to the forest and the nearby village to collect the required materials for *shraad*. Devi Sita kept waiting at the bank of Phalgu River; however, none of them returned. The time of *pind-daan* was nearing, Devi Sita was now worried as the ceremony must be performed before noon.

At that time, she noticed that the soul of King Dasharatha appeared and asked for *pind-daan*. Still, there was no trace of Lord Rama and Lakshman. At this point, Devi Sita decided to perform *pind-daan* by herself by all possible means. She took a bath in River Phalgu, lit a lamp and made offerings to the dead ancestors. After the rituals, the soul of King Dasharatha blessed Devi Sita and departed with satisfaction. When all this was happening, there were five witnesses to this event of *pind-daan* by Devi Sita to King Dasharatha -

1. The Phalgu River
2. The Akshay Vatam (Banyan Tree, a Sacred tree)
3. A Cow
4. The Brahmin
5. The Fire

After some time when Lord Rama and Lakshman returned, Devi Sita explained them the entire incident. However, the brothers didn't believe her. Devi Sita was upset on seeing their denial, she then called all her five witnesses to confirm the truth. To her surprise, only Akshay Vatam told the truth. River Phalgu, Cow, Fire, and Brahmin denied having seen anything related to *pind-daan* performed by Devi Sita. She was very angry, but she kept quiet.

Without wasting much time, Rama and Lakshman started the *pind-daan* rituals again. However, within a few moments, *Akashvaani* ('celestial announcement', or 'voice from the sky/heaven') was heard, "*Devi Sita has already performed the pind-daan and we are very satisfied. We don't need pind-daan again.*" This *Akashvaani* was by the soul of King Dasharatha and proof of Devi Sita's act. Both Rama and Lakshman felt ashamed for not believing Devi Sita.

Upset Devi Sita then cursed that hereafter River Phalghu would flow only underground at Gaya. She cursed the Cow that hereafter it would no longer be worshipped from the front but only its backside would be worshipped; also, the Cow's mouth will remain impure. She cursed Fire that whatever came in contact with it will be destroyed. She cursed the Brahmin that he would never be satisfied.

Devi Sita then blessed Akshay Vatam (Banyan Tree) to remain immortal and whoever came to Gaya for *pind-daan,* would perform *pind-daan* at Akshay Vatam too.

River Phalghu is a geological mystery as its river bed cannot hold water even during monsoon season, even if all other rivers in the neighbourhood are flooding. Another wonder is that although the river has no surface water, even in summers, water is found a few feet below sand. It is with this water that *pind-daan* is done at any time of the day, at any time of the year.

4

GANESHA'S ANGER

Lord Ganesha is the son of Lord Shiva and Goddess Parvati. He is the brother of Lord Karthikeya. He is one of the most prayed deities in the Hindu religion. Lord Ganesha is known for removing obstacles and is prayed by followers before any auspicious function. He is known as a soft-spoken and loveable God.

Once Lord Brahma and Lord Shiva were in Kailash for some discussion. Both brothers, Lord Ganesha and Lord Karthikeya were playing nearby. Narada Muni (Saint) came there and offered Lord Shiva a beautiful fruit. When the brothers saw the fruit, they began to argue and started fighting and shouting for the fruit. After seeing the brothers quarrel, Lord Shiva intervened and asked Lord Brahma to decide on who shall have the new fruit - Ganesha or Karthikeya?

Lord Brahma, who was known to be wise and fair, who was responsible for creating this world, without taking much time took his decision. He said, "I will choose Karthikeya to have this fruit. The reason behind it is that he is the younger son. Ganesha is the elder brother and should sacrifice for his younger brother."

When Ganesha heard Lord Brahma's decision, he became very upset and decided to teach Lord Brahma a lesson. When Lord Brahma left the place, Ganesha chased Lord Brahma. Eventually, when Ganesha found an appropriate place where Lord Brahma was alone, he transformed himself into a petrifying monster. He then stood in front of Lord Brahma and started making terrifying sounds and gestures to scare him. But Lord Brahma was not scared by this and moved on.

Chandra, the Moon God witnessed this event where Ganesha had transformed himself into a monster and tried to scare Lord Brahma. Moon could not stop his laughter and felt funny about Ganesha. The moon in the sky started laughing aloud on seeing pot-bellied Ganesha with his squat feet and elephant head. Moon was always proud of his beauty; during those days the moon was full throughout the month.

After seeing this, Ganesha, who was visibly annoyed and angry, shouted at the Moon, "I have done nothing wrong with you, and you are laughing at me. Do you think you are handsome? I curse you to turn black and never show your face again." Moon immediately understood that he has messed up with the wrong person. Moon literally got scared and started crying after hearing this terrible curse. The moon apologized and sought pardon from Ganesha. When Ganesha recognized the moon's genuineness, he extended forgiveness. But, once a curse is pronounced, it cannot be taken back, even by God; however, it can be altered.

Ganesha then changed the curse and said that the moon would undergo regular buffing and fading to remind him to be humble. This meant the moon would reduce in appearance, and there would be only one day with no moon in the sky. That day would be called Amavasya, and on the following days, the moon would keep increasing in size and finally on the fifteenth day, it would be of full size, i.e. full moon day. Ganesha further altered his curse, since the moon had made fun of him on Chaturthi day, for thereafter, anyone who looked at the moon on Chaturthi would face difficulties and false allegations.

Chandra (moon) finally bowed his head thankfully. It is said that since that day the moon decreases in size before the no-moon day and increases till the full moon day. I know science has a different explanation, but I am sure you would have enjoyed the other version as well.

5

VILLAGE BURIED IN SAND

This is the story of Alamelamma, who was the wife of King Tirumalaraja. During the 16th century, he was the ruler of Srirangapatna and the heir of Vijayanagara dynasty. The Raja of Mysore, Raja Wadiyar and King Tirumalaraja fought a battle at Kesere near Mysore. Raja Wadiyar won that battle and Srirangaptna Kingdom, which was an island formed by the Kaveri River in Karnataka. King Tirumalaraja, along with his wife Alamelamma moved to Talakadu, and later, he died due to disease. Alamelamma owned many precious pieces of jewellery with her. She was a devotee of Sri Ranga Nayaki, the ensemble of Sri Ranganatha of Srirangapatna temple. Every year, once she used to send her jewels to Sri Ranga Nayaki; on other days, they were kept in Alamelamma's custody.

Raja Wadiyar had a desire to get the possession of these pieces of jewellery in his palace and thus, he ordered his army men to get the custody of the jewellery from Alamelamma. One day, she was chased by Wadiyar's army men to retrieve the jewels. She ran to the cliff overlooking the Kaveri River and jumped into the river at a place called Malangi, keeping the rest of her jewels tied up in a cloth. Before jumping to death below was the curse uttered by Alamelamma –

"*Talakadu maralagali, Malangi maduvagali, Mysuru doregalige makkalilllade hogali.*" This means "Let the city of Talakad turn into sand, let the Malangi turn into a whirlpool, let the Rajas of Mysore not have children for eternity."

So, let's get into the details of the three curses by Alamelamma -

- Talakadu maralagali - Let the city of Talakad turn into sand

The Talakad city was abandoned by residents and buried under sand. If you visit Talakad, even today you will see many temples buried in sand.

- Malangi maduvagali - Let the Malangi turn into a whirlpool

Vigorous torrents and formation of whirlpools, big or small are a common sight at Malangi River.

- Mysuru doregalige makkalilllade hogali - Let the Rajas of Mysore not have children for eternity

The curse was alive for almost 400 years, with successive kings having no children and adopting their family members (cousins or nephews) to take over the throne over generations. This could be the debatable curse now as the current Maharaja of Mysuru, Yaduveer Krishnadatta Chamaraja Wodeyar and his wife Trishika Kumari were blessed with a baby boy in 2017. Interestingly, Yaduveer is an adopted son of the preceding queen Pramoda Devi, who adopted him as she and her late husband Srikantadatta Narasimharaja Wodeyar did not have any children of their own.

Over generations, Wodeyars (Wadiyars) have tried to conciliate Alamelamma and reverse the curse. Raja Wodeyar even put up an idol of Alamelamma in Mysore. Even today, Alamelamma's idol can be found inside the Mysore Palace and is worshiped by the royal family.

Even though many historians, geologists, archeologists, and scientists have different versions about sand in Talakad, Malangi's whirlpools and lack of heirs in the royal family. No one can tell whether these stories are all made up or not.

6

LEGENDS OF ALAH

Once upon a time, there lived two brothers, Alah and Udal. Udal was the younger brother of Alah. They were generals in the army of Raja Parimal of the Chandel Kingdom. Both the brothers were true warriors in the real sense as no one could defeat them in a war skill. They fought many kings and were the most prominent sword fighters in the Bundelkhand region.

Once the great Rajput king Prithviraj Chouhan went to battle against Chandel as he wanted to expand his supremacy in the region. Alah and Udal led Chandel's army and fought like lions. Both the brothers withered the entire army of Prithviraj Chouhan. However, Udal got killed in the combat. Alah eventually got hold of the great Prithviraj Chouhan and after heavy sword fight, brought him down on his knees. As Alah was about to cut off Prithviraj's head, his guru Gorakhnath came in the way. Gorakhnath told Alah that he should spare the life of Prithviraj as he would change the lives of many people from his Rajput community and state. Alah then spared the life of Prithviraj and left for the forest.

Alah was a devotee of Goddess Sharda. In the forest, he worshipped her for 12 years, and one day, Goddess Sharda appeared in his dream and asked his head as a sacrifice. He informed about his dream to the King and the General. All of them stopped Alah from following Goddess Sharda's request as it was just a dream. But Alah was a great devotee and did not pay heed to anyone's advice. He cut off his head with his sword and offered to Goddess Sharda, who was pleased with this act of Alah and made him immortal.

It is believed that even today Alah visits Goddess Sharda's shrine in Maihar, Madhya Pradesh to offer his prayers. No one is allowed to offer prayers before 4 am as it is said that Alah comes daily between 2 to 4 am and offers *pooja* to Goddess Sharda in Maihar. When the doors are opened at 4am, a lamp will be lit, there will be fresh flowers at Goddess' feet, and water filled in a bowl next to Goddess's idol. It is also believed that without Alah's offerings, the Goddess does not accept anyone's offerings. Strange story, right? I suggest you to visit Maihar once to witness this unbelievable act.

7

SACRIFICE OF DHARAMPADA

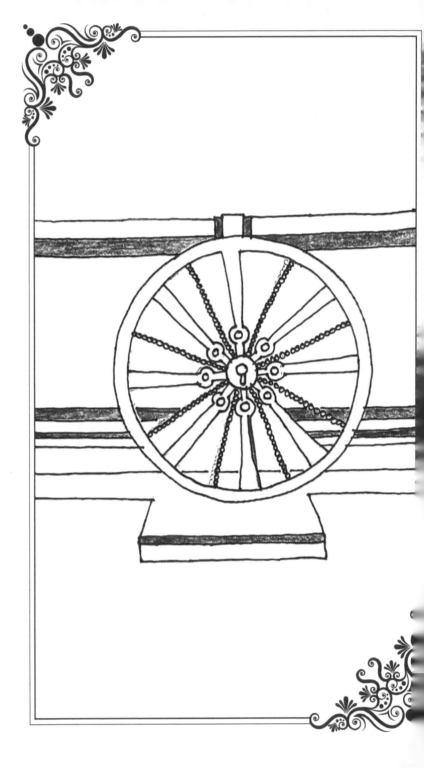

During the 12th Century, there lived a great temple architect Bisu Maharana. His son's name was Dharampada. Before Dharampada was born, his father Bisu had to leave for construction work of the Sun Temple at Konark. Even though his father was not around during his childhood, Dharampada got access to many manuscripts on temple construction, and by the time he was 12, he knew the art of Odiya temple architecture very well.

This temple was getting built by the King Narshinghdev, it was King's order that no one would be allowed to go away until the whole work was completed. The temple was supposed to get completed in 12 years with 12 thousand craftsmen. As Bisu Maharana was the chief architect of the Sun Temple of Konark, he could not leave the place for 12 years, and Dharmapada could not meet his father for those 12 years.

Dharmapada always missed his father and wanted to see him. On his 12th birthday, he asked his mother a gift - a chance to meet his father. His mother could not refuse this demand of her son. So, after taking his mother's blessings, Dharmapada started a journey to meet his father. After a few days of travel, he reached the construction site of Konark temple, where he met his father. Both father and son were happy to see each other for the first time. However, this happiness didn't last long when Bisu Maharana informed Dharampada about the major problem they were facing with temple construction. Construction of the temple was almost done; however, they were finding difficulties in placing the keystone or Kalasha on the top of the temple. They only had 12 hours left to finish this work, else the King Narshinghdev would be angry and kill all 12000 craftsmen without thinking twice. The deadline for completing temple construction was nearing, and all were tensed. They tried their knowledge to move the Kalasha on top, but nothing worked.

Dharmapada wanted to help his father, he had the knowledge of temple architecture which he had gathered during his early childhood days. After an hour of inspection, Dharmpada got a solution and came with the design of the keystone which would hold the temple together. When Bisu saw the design, he was pleasantly surprised and happy seeing his son's skill. Immediately, he gave the nod to implement the solution proposed by Dharmapada. By mid-night the keystone was on top of the temple and construction was completed. All were relieved. Dharmapada was still on top of the temple when he heard the whispers of the people gathered to see the completed work. They all feared that if the King comes to know that a 12-year-old boy has completed the temple work and not 12000 craftsmen which the King had employed, he may order to kill all craftsmen involved in construction work including Bisu.

Dharmapada who was listening to all these conversations and concerns from the top of the temple, decided to save the lives of 12000 people, including his father. He was not hungry for fame or wanted glory for self by completing the keystone work. He decided to end his life so that others can be saved. By then it was time when the first rays of the sun started falling on the temple; it looked like Sun God was showering all his blessings on the temple. With a heavy heart, Dharmpada jumped off the temple top into the sea. Everyone standing there was stunned seeing the courage of a 12-year-old child.

Later, Dharampada became an integral part of Oriya art and immortal for Indian art.

8

SURDAS AND RADHA'S ANKLETS

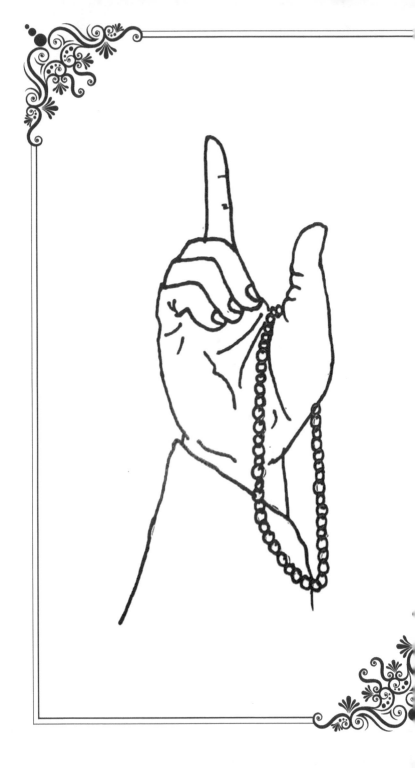

During the 15th Century, there lived a great saint, poet, and musician called *Sant* Surdas. He was blind by birth. He was famous for his devotion and dedication to Lord Krishna. There are different tales about his birthplace; some say he was born in Siri Village near Delhi, and many believe he was born in Mathura. Once Surdas dreamt of Krishna, and in his dream, Krishna asked him to go to Vrindavan and dedicate his life to Krishna.

In Vrindavan, he met Shri Vallabharacharya, who later became Surdas's Guru. Surdas requested Shri Vallabharacharya to accept him as his disciple. Even though Surdas had many good qualities, he had an issue with his anger and was very short-tempered. Vallabharacharya knew about this and wanted to make Surdas his disciple once Surdas get rid of his anger. So Vallabharacharya instructed Surdas to hymn Lord Krishna's name while doing all the tasks for one month and to then come back to meet him. He would then decide whether to make him his disciple. As Surdas was quite eager to learn spirituality, he followed his Guru's instruction.

After one month, Surdas went to meet his Guru. On his way, when he was walking on the road, one sweeper accidentally put dirt on his clothes. As Surdas was short-tempered, he got very angry and scolded the sweeper loudly. He then went back home, changed his clothes and returned to meet his Guru. When Surdas reached the Guru's place, his Guru told him he was not yet ready to be his disciple and learn spiritualty. He asked Surdas to go back, continue chanting Lord Krishna's name and come again after one month.

One month passed by and again after 30 days, Surdas decided to meet his Guru. He was again approaching the same road when the sweeper once again put dirt on Surdas. This time Surdas was furious and scolded the sweeper even louder than the last time. He then went back to his home, changed his clothes and returned to meet his Guru. Again Shri Vallabharacharya sent Surdas back home and asked him to come back after one month.

By now, Surdas had realised what's wrong with him. After one month, the same incident repeated when Surdas was on his way to meet his Guru. When the sweeper put dirt on Surdas, this time, instead of getting angry, Surdas thanked the sweeper and said, "I am thankful to you as you have helped me to overcome my anger."

This time when he reached his Guru's *Ashram*, his Guru was waiting for him. Shri Vallabharacharya hugged Surdas and said, "Now you are ready to learn spirituality and I accept you as my disciple." This was the beginning of Surdas's spiritual journey, and he attained fame for his devotion towards Lord Krishna.

One day, Surdas fell into a well and was stuck there for a long time. He then started chanting Lord Krishna's name and prayed for rescue. Lord Krishna came and rescued Surdas from the well. Radha was very curious and wanted to know why Krishna always helped Surdas whenever he was in trouble. To this, Lord Krishna answered that he was very happy with Surdas' devotion towards him and would always be with him during any need of hour.

One day, Radha decided to test the spiritual power of Surdas and went near him. Surdas recognized the divine movement and pulled Radha's anklets in his hand. Embarrassed Radha asked him to return her anklets, but Surdas refused to do so. Then Radha revealed her identity and asked him to return her anklets. However, Surdas refused stating that he could not believe her as he is blind. Now visibly worried Radha called Krishna for rescue. Krishna gave vision to Surdas's eyes and this made Surdas see both Krishna and Radha. Krishna told Surdas that he was very happy with his dedication and devotion for Krishna and allowed Surdas to ask for any wish he wanted.

Surdas returned Radha's anklets and requested Krishna to make him blind again as he didn't want to see anything else in his life after seeing Krishna. Radha was moved by this kind of devotion and tears flowed down from her eyes. Krishna granted Surdas's wish and made him blind again, thus making him eternal.

9

KAK MAHAL

Once upon a time, there lived Prince Rana Mahendra of Umer Kot. Mahendra was a very good hunter and went hunting in jungles very often. In Jaisalmer, there lived one Rajput Princess, Mumal. She was very beautiful and charming. She wanted to marry a guy who was brave and intelligent. Hence, to test the skills of the men who wanted to marry Mumal, she, along with her sisters and female attendants, would weave a web of magic in the palace which was called the Kak Mahal. Many kings and princes tried to break the magic of Kak Mahal, but it was always in vain.

Once while hunting, Mahendra came near Kak Mahal; he got attracted towards the palace. At that moment, Mumal saw Mahendra from her palace and got attracted towards him. She conveyed the message to Mahendra through her servant, and challenged him if he could reach her palace by crossing all the magical mazes and hurdles. Mahendra accepted the challenge and through his courage and brilliance crossed all riddles and reached the palace. Mumal was impressed with Mahendra. Eventually, both fell in love; Mahendra spent few days in Jaisalmer to spend time with Mumal and later returned to Umer Kot.

Once back in Umer Kot, he could not resist meeting Mumal again; however distance between Jaisalmer and Umer Kot was around 129 miles. It was not easy to cover such a distance quickly during those days. Mahendra found one camel named Cheetal which was very fast and could cover long distances in a short time. Mahendra used this camel to travel from Umer Kot to Kak Mahal. This camel only took few hours to cover the distance between Umer Kot and Kak Mahal. This way Mahendra and Mumal started meeting each other every night.

One day, Mahendra's family came to know about the relationship between Mahendra and Mumal. They also found out how Mahendra was using a camel to reach Jaisalmer every night. In a fit of rage, they broke the legs of Cheetal. On that night, Mahendra arranged another camel to reach Jaisalmer. As this new camel was not familiar with the route, in the dark, Mahendra couldn't figure out the way and instead of Jaisalmer, they reached Barmer. Upon realising that they have reached the wrong place, Mahendra again started for Jaisalmer from Barmer.

Meanwhile, at Kak Mahal, Mumal was waiting for Mahendra. All her sisters were with her to give her company till Mahendra arrived. Mumal's sisters decided to play a game and one of the sisters Sumal dressed up like a man. After some time, all were tired and ended up sleeping in their rooms. However, Sumal, who was dressed in the man's attire, slept with Mumal on her bed. When Mahendra reached Kak Mahal and saw this, he was very angry and offended; he felt that Mumal had cheated him. He decided to leave his riding cane beside Mumal's bed and left.

When Mumal came to know about Mahendra's visit, she followed Mahendra and tried to explain him that there was no man in her bed, but he was reluctant to understand anything. All the pleadings of Mumal went in vain. Mumal could not think of her life without Mahendra and to prove her innocence, she set a fire and jumped into the flames. Mahendra rushed to save her but it was too late; her entire body was burning in fire. As he was still in love with her, without giving a second thought, Mahendra too jumped in the fire, and both died together. Hence making their love story eternal and legendary in India.

10

KULDHARA: THE ABANDONED VILLAGE

Kuldhara is a small village, around 15 km south-west of Jaisalmer, Rajasthan. Centuries ago, this village was abandoned by its residents. Yes, the entire village was abandoned overnight by some thousand-odd residents for some known and unknown reasons. As per mythological stories, there is a curse on Kuldhara village which does not let anyone live there ever since it was abandoned by the villagers.

Around 200 years ago, Paliwal Brahmins used to live in Kuldhara. The name Kuldhara is derived from the word "Kuldhar" which was the name of a sub-caste of Paliwal Brahmins. All the villagers were happy and prosperous. It is said that the Diwan or the Prime Minister of Jaisalmer, Salim Singh, fell in love with a girl of Kuldhara who was the daughter of the Village Chief.

Salim Singh wanted to marry that girl, but the Village Chief rejected the proposal as both were from different castes. Salim Singh, who was infamous for his wicked lifestyle and immoral ways of collecting tax, threatened to prosecute the Kuldhara Brahmins if he was not allowed to marry the chief's girl. He sent an ultimatum and warning to the villagers that they must accept the marriage proposal or be ready to face war.

Paliwal Brahmins were not like Kshatriyas who could go for war with Salim's army men. Instead of fighting and losing their pride, Paliwals decided to abandon the village. One dark night all the Brahmins Paliwals gathered at one place in Kuldhara. They carried all their belongings; however, they buried all the precious treasures within the village and abandoned their houses.

Before leaving the village, all the Brahmins put a curse on Kuldhara village that no one would be able to settle in this village ever again. This curse was to protect the treasures they had buried there, hopeful that they may come back someday and dig it out again. Nobody knows where they went, but some believed that Paliwals settled near Jodhpur which was another city in Rajasthan.

There is another version of the story where it is said that around 200 years ago, most of the wells in and around Kuldhara dried up and water table went down. There was no other source of water to meet irrigation and drinking requirements. The scarcity of underground water supply could have led Paliwals to abandon Kuldhara and migrate to a different place.

Today, Kuldhara is a heritage site that is maintained by the Archaeological Survey of India.

11

RIVER KAVERI IN KAMANDALU

Once in South India, there was an unusually hot summer and the situation was getting worse due to drought. Without rains, all rivers, ponds, and lakes had dried up. With no water, animals and humans started dying. Sage Agastya was worried by seeing the situation of the people who were suffering due to non-availability of water. He decided to go to the Himalayas and pray to Lord Shiva to find the solution. Once he reached the Himalayas, he started *tapasya*. Finally, one day Lord Shiva appeared in front of him and asked him his wish. Sage Agastya asked him for an unlimited supply of the pure waters of Kailasa in his kamandalu (brass pot) which he could carry anywhere he wanted. Lord Shiva agreed and gave him this boon. In return, Shiva asked Agastya one favour. He said that due to arrogance, Vindhya mountains were rising too wild and high, and this was posing a challenge to the Himalayas. Hence, the Vindhya mountains' growth should be stalled. The sage agreed to help Lord Shiva in this matter.

While returning, Sage Agastya reached the foothills of Vindhya mountains which are in northern India. They had grown so huge that the Sage could not find any way to cross the mountain. On seeing Agastya, Vindhya, the mountain bowed down to concede the presence of the great sage and asked what he could do for him.

Seeing the correct opportunity, the Sage told Vindhya that he wanted to cross the mountain to go to the other side and asked him to bend down further to make way for his movement. Vindhya immediately followed this request and bowed down. The Sage then crossed the mountains; he then asked Vindhya to remain in the current form till he returned. Vindhya, without any hesitation, agreed to follow the instruction from the Sage. This was the trap by Sage Agastya, he never returned back and Vindhya Mountains remained in bowed position and never grown higher than Himalayas. Sage Agastya kept his promise given to Lord Shiva.

Sage Agastya carrying the pure waters of Kailasa in his kamandalu (brass pot) was looking for an appropriate place down south to start the river. He reached the hilly Coorg region, where he decided to take some rest as he was tired. He saw one small boy playing nearby. It was Lord Ganesha disguised as a boy. Sage Agastya called him to hold the kamandalu carefully while he took rest for some time and that he would later find an appropriate place to start the river. Once Sage Agastya slept, Lord Ganesha, in his wisdom, selected the right place for the origin of the river and left the kamandalu on the ground at the spot and disappeared.

After some time, one crow came and toppled the kamandalu; this caused the water to spill out from the kamandalu. As the kamandalu fell and made a noise, the Sage woke up and shooed away the crow. By now the sacred water had spilled from the kamandalu, and the water gushing out was the sacred River Kaveri flowing from the spot, now known as Talakaveri. Talakaveri is near Brahmagiri hills of the Western Ghats in the Kodagu district of Karnataka.

12

UNAKOTI

Unakoti is situated in Tripura; a considerable part of this place is jungles. In this place, you will find less than a crore stone images and carvings. This is one of the major tourist attractions. You will also see a 30-feet high Shiva statue called Unakotiswara Kaal Bhairava.

There is a folktale associated with this place. once Lord Shiva was travelling to Kashi, he was accompanied by an entourage of deities. These deities, including Shiva numbered at One Crore. After a long journey, they reached Unakoti and decided to rest for the night. As Lord Shiva didn't want to delay his journey to Kashi, he requested all the Gods and Goddesses to wake up early morning before sunrise so that they could continue their journey.

The next day, except Shiva the rest of the deities were asleep even after sunrise. No other Gods and Goddesses could wake up as instructed by Shiva. This made Lord Shiva angry, and he cursed all the deities who were asleep and turned all of them to stones. The Lord Shiva continued his journey to Kashi on his own. Hence, a crore minus one Gods and Goddesses turned to stone that day, and this place got its name as Unakoti.

I am sure a few of the readers may not be able to relate this story with reality. So, let me share another legend on Unakoti. Once upon a time, there lived a person named Kalu Kumar; he was a local sculptor and potter. He was a big devotee of Goddess Parvati. Kalu always had a desire to be in Kailash with Goddess Parvati and Lord Shiva to serve them and be there for the rest of his life in their abode. For this, once he performed a *havan* for 21 days to impress Goddess Parvati. Parvati was impressed with his devotion and acknowledged to take Kalu to Kailash. However, to have Kalu's wish fulfilled even Lord Shiva must give permission. Lord Shiva agreed with one condition, and the condition was that if Kalu would sculpt a Koti (One Million) images of Lord Shiva and other deities in one night and before sunrise, only then Kalu's wish will be fulfilled.

The day was decided when Kalu would start sculpting. He was confident of finishing Koti (one million) sculptures in one night. However, fate had something else written for him. Kalu worked the whole night determinedly, but before sunrise he could only sculpt one less than a million idols. Hence, disappointed Kalu left that place with one million minus one idols sculpted on stones and the place's name is called Unakoti.

13

QUEEN OF SNAKES

Once there lived an eminent Sage, Jagatakaru. He used to follow strict penance and refrain himself from marriage. One day when he was wandering in the jungle, he came to a place where he found few men hanging on a tree upside-down with a rope. They were Jagatakaru's ancestors. Upon realising this, he asked them what made them be in this gloom condition? They explained to him that as all their children being dead, no one had performed the last rites for them. The only hope for them was Jagatakaru who could help them get free by getting married, and thus his child could perform the last rites and set all the ancestors free.

On seeing the pathetic condition of his ancestors, Jagatakaru agreed to marry on a condition that the parents of the girl, who he would marry, should give her willingly. Vasuki, the king of snakes, was there when the conversation between Jagatakaru and his ancestors was going on. Vasuki offered his sister Manasa to the sage. Jagatakaru married Manasa and had one son, Asika. Asika performed the last rites of the ancestors and relieved them.

Manasa was the queen of snakes; she was also known as Vishahara, 'the destroyer of poison'. She was considered as the protectress of men from reptiles.

Once there lived a merchant named Chanda, he didn't believe in Manasa's power and refused to worship her. Chanda was prompt in disregarding Manasa as a Goddess. This made Manasa angry; she was extremely furious at those who refused to worship her and was very kind to those who worshipped her. Eventually, six of Chanda's sons died from snake bites. By seeing the death of all his brothers, Chanda's eldest son Lakindara started living in an iron house to ensure no snake entered his house. However, Manasa ensured that a snake enters the house, and on his wedding day, he was bitten by a snake and he died.

However, Lakindara's widow escaped and went to her mother-in-law, Chanda's wife. By now all knew that it's due to Manasa's anger that so much bad and evil things had happened to their family, and it's high time to get her blessings to reverse her curse. All the family members and neighbours urged Chanda to leave his ego and appease Goddess Manasa. Manasa herself didn't want to trouble Chanda further but wished that he should realise his mistakes. After a lot of push and requests from his family members, Chanda yielded to their wishes and threw one flower with his left hand towards Manasa's image. This was enough for Manasa who was delighted by Chanda's offering and restored his sons' lives. With this incident, people came to know the power of the snake queen Manasa, and she was worshipped for her blessings. She is worshiped generally during rainy season as snakes are very active during this time.

14

HASTAMALAKA: THE DISCIPLE OF ADI SHANKARACHARYA

Once during the 9th Century, Adi Shankaracharya was travelling with his disciple in the southern part of India. During their travel, they reached one village Sri Bali, near Udupi. When residents of the village came to know about his presence, all of them went to meet him and seek his blessings. Among these villagers, there was one Brahmin named Prabhakara. He had a 13-year-old boy who never spoke a word. Hence everyone, including his parents, believed that he was a lunatic. When Prabhakara met Adi Shankaracharya, he requested him to see his son and bless him.

As soon as Adi Shankaracharya saw the boy, he knew that the child was spiritually advanced. He asked the boy, "Child, who are you? Where are you coming from?" To this, the boy chanted Hastamalaka Stotram. It's a sublime Advaita philosophy explained in few Sanskrit verses.

The boy's parents were shocked and happily surprised to know that their son not only spoke but had divine knowledge as well. However, they were wondering how their 13-year-old boy had gained so much knowledge without talking all these years. To this Adi Shankaracharya explained that once when the child was small, his mother had taken him to a river. Unknowingly, the child drowned in the river and died. One sage was witnessing this incident, he could not imagine how sad the boy's parents would be after losing him. So, he decided to leave his own body and entered the dead child's body, hence making the boy alive. By this the boy got all the wisdom and knowledge which the sage had.

Adi Shankaracharya, with the boy's parents' consent, made him his disciple and took the boy along with him. He named the boy Hastamalaka, which means one who has the knowledge of Brahma comfortably as *amla* (gooseberry) in his hand. He was the creator of Hastamalaka Strotram.

15

ASHTAVAKRA:
THE VEDIC SAGE

Once upon a time, there lived one Rishi Uddalaka, he had great knowledge of Vedas. He had many disciples; among them Kahoda was his favourite disciple. Uddalaka married his only daughter Sujata to Kahoda. Both Kahoda and Sujata continued to stay in the hermitage of Uddalaka even after marriage. Kahoda joined Uddalaka to teach new disciples within the hermitage.

After a few years, Sujata became pregnant. During her pregnancy period, she used to sit near her father and husband whenever they taught their disciples. Due to this, Sujata's unborn child gained mastery of the Vedas, mainly by listening to his grandfather Uddalaka. Kohada, however, was not as skilled as his teacher and made few errors while teaching Vedic Mantra. By now, the unborn child knew all the Vedic mantras and could not resist pinpointing the errors made by his father. One day, this child, who was still in the womb, told his father who was teaching his disciples that while reciting the Vedic mantra his father was making a few errors. Kahoda could not bear the insult and cursed that the child would be born with eight bends or deformities in his body. When the child was born, he did have eight deformations, and he was named Ashtavakra.

Meanwhile, Kahoda moved to Mithila Kingdom which was ruled by King Janaka. As time passed by, once there came one Brahmin named Vandin from *Varunaloka* (world of water bodies) and challenged King Janaka if anyone from Mithila could beat him in '*shastraarth*' (a verbal duel or competition among learned and wise on the meaning on Vedic scriptures). If he won, he would take the defeated learned ones to Varunaloka and keep them captive. Janaka agreed to this challenge and asked all the sages and knowledgeable people to participate in *shastraarth* with the Brahmin. However, whoever accepted the challenge was defeated by the Brahmin and was immersed and prisoned in *Varunaloka*. Kahoda also accepted the challenge and had the same fate as others. He made the same mistakes that Ashtavakra had pointed out to him when Ashtavakra was in his mother's womb. Kahoda too was defeated by Vandin and got imprisoned in *Varunaloka*.

Ashtavakra was 10 years old then. When he came to know about his father's imprisonment in *Varunaloka*, he decided to go to Mithila and free his father. Ashtavakra reached Mithila and met King Janaka in his palace. After initial reluctance, King Janaka realised that Ashtavakra is a great and wise sage and has great knowledge of Vedas and scriptures. He immediately arranged a *shastraarth* between Ashtavakra and Vandin.

Ashtavakra defeated Vandin in *shastraarth*; as per the contest conditions, the winner can ask any wish from Vandin. Ashtavakra commanded Vandin be drowned in river water as it was done to his earlier *shastraarth's* opponents. Upon this, Vandin revealed to Ashtavakra that he is the son of Varuna, the god of all water bodies. He further explained that Varuna was performing a big *yagna* in *Varunaloka* and wanted a large number of learned people to perform the same. All the people whom he had drowned were safe in *Varunaloka*. Ashtavakra then demanded Vandin to bring back all the people from Varunaloka to Mithila, which he agreed immediately.

All the people who were drowned by Vandin came back to Mithila at King Janaka's court where everyone were present. After seeing his son, Kahoda was very pleased and happy; however after seeing Ashtavakra's deformed body, he felt sad about cursing his son and decided to reverse the curse. On the way back home, Kahoda asked Ashtavakra to take a dip in the River Samanga. By doing so, Ashtavakra was freed from all the eight deformations.

Later, Ashtavakra went to become a great rishi and a self-realised soul. King Janaka became the disciple of Ashtavakra, who showed him the path of enlightenment. Ashtavakra Gita or Ashtavakra Samhita, which has 20 chapters, are the teachings of Ashtavakra given to King Janaka. It is a classical Advaita Vedanta scripture and mainly a dialogue between Ashtavakra and King Janaka on the nature of soul, reality and bondage.

16

VERMILION: THE SYMBOL OF MARRIAGE

During 100 BC, there lived a tribe called Oraon; they still exist in many Indian states. This tribe calls themselves Kurukh, perhaps after a legendary Oraon king called Karakh. This story is of four friends during 100 BC. From childhood, all the four friends played, ate and lived together. Their friendship was famous in the entire tribe and nearby villages.

When they grew up, all four took different professions to start earning their livelihood and decided to go to new places. One of them became a weaver, the second became a goldsmith, the third became a vermilion hawker, and the fourth one took wood carving as his profession. They all used to travel together and work at the same place on their respective skills.

Once during their travel, they reached a mango orchard in the evening and decided to spend that night there. As it was unknown territory for them, post-dinner, they decided that it's better to keep a watch entire night in turns to avoid any theft of their valuables. First, it was the wood carver's turn to keep the vigil while the other three friends went to sleep.

After some time, the wood carver noticed a big log of wood lying nearby. He decided to carve the wood and make something out of it. Within an hour, he had chiselled the wood into a female figure; he was very happy with his craft. As it was the weaver's turn to do the vigilance, the wood carver woke the weaver up and went to sleep. When the weaver saw a beautiful wooden female figure, he was very impressed and decided to weave a perfect sari for it. Within one hour he made a sari and wrapped her. Now it was the goldsmith's turn to wake up and replace the weaver. The weaver woke up the goldsmith and slept. The goldsmith spotted a wooden female figure with a sari. He admired her and thought something was missing. "Oh yeah, ornaments are missing," he spoke to himself. He then made a gold necklace, earrings and bangles, put all of them on her. Now, the look of the wooden female figure was no less than an *Apsara*. The goldsmith was now tired and woke up the vermilion hawker before retiring to sleep. When the hawker saw a wooden woman, it was dawn, and he smeared her forehead with vermilion. Immediately, the wooden woman came alive; she was shy and charmingly beautiful.

By now, all four friends were awake from sleep, and on seeing a beautiful girl, they started to quarrel on marrying the girl. All of them had justifications for marrying the girl. The wood carver said that had he not used his skill to craft the wood then she would not have come in existence at all. The weaver said that because he gave clothes to her hence he should marry her. Similarly, the goldsmith claimed that he had given valuable gold ornaments to her so it's his right to marry her and the hawker said that because his action of putting vermilion on her forehead brought her to life, he is the right person to marry her.

As the heated argument continued for some time, they didn't arrive at a proper conclusion. During this time, a holy sage was passing by, and they decided to call him to seek his decision to whom should the girl marry. The holy sage heard all about the incident that had happened the previous night till morning. He then agreed to be the arbitrator for them. He said that as the wood carver is the creator of the girl, he is her father, the weaver gave her clothes hence he is her brother, the goldsmith gave her gold so he is her uncle, and finally who gave life to the girl by putting vermilion on her forehead is her husband, that is the vermilion hawker. All four friends agreed to this decision, and the hawker married the girl.

Vermilion or Sindur is a symbol of marriage in the Hindu religion, and only married women apply it along the parting hair. It is applied in the center and symbolizes female energy.

17

THE POWER OF AATMA LINGA

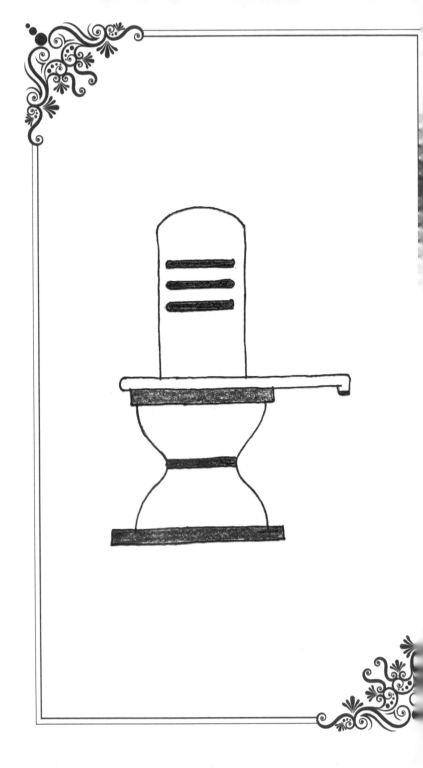

Ravana was a great Shiva devotee; he was born to a Brahmin father and Rakshasa mother. He always wanted to attain immortality and insuperability. To accomplish this, the only way was to get hold of *Aatma Linga*, which was the soul or essence of Lord Shiva. Ravana was an ardent devotee of Lord Shiva. He decided to pray to Lord Shiva and get the *Aatma Linga* from the Lord. He decided to go for penance in Mount Kailash and started his *yagna* for Lord Shiva. He recited *Shivatandavastotram* which won Lord Shiva's heart and he appeared in front of Ravana. Lord Shiva asked Ravana for a boon, to which Ravana asked for *Aatma linga*. Shiva agreed to give him the *Aatma Linga*; however there was one condition. The condition was that *Aatma Linga* should not be placed on the ground. If it happens then *Aatma Linga* will establish itself wherever it is placed on earth, and all the power of *Aatma Linga* will return to Lord Shiva.

Ravana understood the condition and obtained the *Aatma Linga* from Lord Shiva and started his journey to Lanka. Sage Narada, who was closely monitoring this incident was now a worried man. He knew if Ravana gets immorality with *Aatma Linga* then he would surely create havoc on earth and would make mankind's life miserable. Hence, he approached Lord Ganesh and sought his help to ensure that Ravana does not take *Aatama Linga* to Lanka. Lord Ganesha knew that Ravana was very punctual about performing daily *pooja* to Lord Shiva and it had been an integral part of Ravana's life.

Meanwhile, Ravana continued his journey with *Aatma Linga*, and he reached a place near the western coast of India; the place now known as Gokarna. Lord

Ganesha requested Lord Vishnu to stain out the sun so that it looks like sunset time, and this was the time when Ravana used to perform *Sandyavandhana*, evening prayer to Lord Shiva. Seeing the darkness, worried Ravana was thinking about how to perform *pooja* without keeping *Aatma Linga* on the ground. At this point, Lord Ganesha disguised himself as a Brahmin boy and stood at some distance from Ravana. On seeing a Brahmin boy, Ravana summoned the boy and asked him to hold *Aatma Linga* till he finished his evening *pooja*. He also instructed him not to place *Aatma Linga* on the ground. The boy was initially reluctant, however, agreed to hold *Aatma Linga* on a condition. The boy said as *Aatma Linga* is heavy he would hold it only until he could, and he would call Ravana thrice before keeping it on the ground. Ravana agreed to this condition.

As it was already planned, as soon as Ravana started his *Sandyavandhana*, the Brahmin boy (Lord Ganesha) called Ravana thrice and placed the *Aatma Linga* on the ground. The Brahmin boy then disappeared, and Vishnu then removed the illusion, and it was broad daylight again. Ravana by now knew he had been cheated. With huge anger, he tried to uproot the *Aatma Linga*. But he could not succeed. Ravana then used his demonic power to extricate the *Aatma Linga*, resulting in throwing the parts of the Linga to five different places which later became famous temples of Lord Shiva. These five temples are Surathkal, Dhareshwar, Gunavanteshwar, Murudeshwar and Shejjeshwar temples.

Ravana had to return to Lanka without *Aatma Linga*.

18

First Naga Prathistta

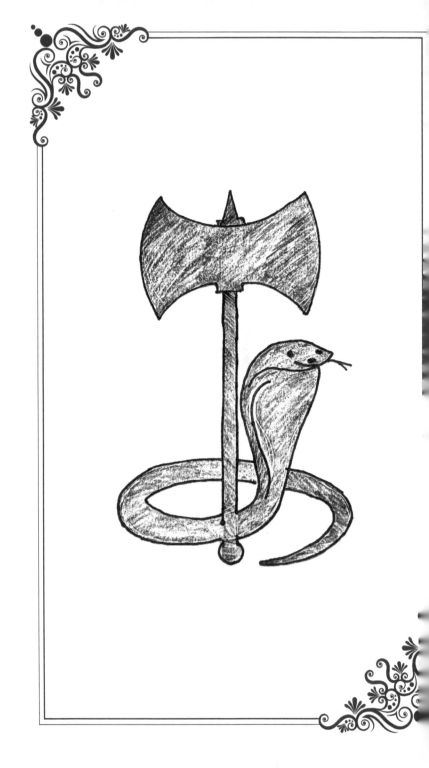

Once there lived King Kartairaveerarjuna. Rishi Jamadagni's Asharam was in Kartairaveerarjuna's Kingdom. Lord Parshurama, who was the fourth child of Renuka and Rishi Jamadagni, is also considered as the sixth incarnation of Lord Vishnu.

Once the King went hunting in a jungle with his army. After hunting, while returning to his kingdom, he decided to take rest in a jungle. The place where they were resting was near Rishi Jamadagni's Asharam. When Rishi came to know about this, he immediately rushed to the place where the King was resting and invited him to his Asharam, along with his army. When the King reached the Asharam, he was surprised to see the hospitality they received. They were served with delicious foods and drinks. The King was really surprised, and he was keen to know how the small Asharam sages managed to make such delicious food in such huge quantity which could serve his entire army that too at such short notice.

The surprised King asked Rishi how he had managed to arrange such hospitality. To this, Rishi revealed the Kamdhenu cow which he had received from Lord Indra. Kamdhenu cow had divine powers and it was due to these qualities of Kamdhenu that the Rishi could arrange food for the King and his army. After seeing Kamdhenu cow at Rishi's Asharam, Kartairaveerarjuna demanded the Rishi to handover the cow to him as it's his kingdom where Kamdhenu was living, and the King had the right to take any property in his kingdom. But Rishi Jamadagni refused to give Kamdhenu to the King. This made Kartairaveerarjuna very angry. He destroyed the Asharam in rage. He then tried to take the holy cow

Kamdhenu with him, but Kamdhenu refused to go with the King and departed from there to heaven with her divine powers. The King was disappointed as he could not get the holy cow and had to return to his kingdom empty-handed.

When Parshurama came, he saw the devasted Asharam. Jamadagni explained to him what had happened. After hearing the incident, Parshurama became very angry and he decided to punish Kartairaveerarjuna. Parshurama accompanied by his weapon 'Parshu' declared war against Kartairaveerarjuna. Even though the King had a huge army of skilled soldiers, but it proved to be a dwarf in front of Parshurama's bravery. Parshurama killed Kartairaveerarjuna and his army during the war. After this, Parshurama based on the instruction from his father, went on pilgrimage to perform penance for this slaughter.

During this time, Kartairaveerarjuna's sons attacked Jamadagni's Asharam and killed Jamadagni to take revenge of their father's killing. When Parshurama came to know about his father's death, he swore to kill all kshatriya generations as they sprung up. He fulfilled his words by killing the Kshatriya clan 21 times and destroyed the kshatriya land. Later, Maharishi Richik requested him to stop this devastation of killing Kshatriyas. Subsequently, Lord Parshurama performed the *shraad* ceremony of his ancestors.

After this, the Kshatriya lands which Parshurama had seized, he gave them to Sage Kashyap. Sage Kashyap is one of the Saptarishis, the seven famed rishis, considered to be the author of many hymns and verses of the Rigveda. As these lands were not fit to live as per Sage Kashyap's request, Parshurama restored a major portion of the land from the sea, and it was the origin of land called Kerala. He then sent Brahmins to live there. However, the land was not fertile due to high content of salt and ore in sand as it had emerged from seawater. This was making the life of Brahmins living there miserable. Hence all the Brahmins requested Parshurama to make the land fertile enough so that they can live in a better ecosystem. On seeing Brahmins in trouble, Parshurama decided to travel to Moutain Gandhamadhana and meditate. Anantha, the Serpent God, who resided there, was pleased with Parshurama. Anantha appeared before Lord Parshurama and blessed him with a boon. Parshurama requested Lord Anantha to make the land of Kerala fertile. Lord Anantha blessed this boon by instructing the Nagas to suck out all the lavana, ores and unwanted items from the land and make the land into a fertile one. All the Nagas followed Anantha's instruction, and within no time, the land was fertile and livable.

Parshurama was very happy with the act of Lord Anantha. As a token of gratitude, he decided to consecrate Lord Anantha in one part of the land (Kerala). He then took guidance of Lord Brahma for *muhoortham* (Hindu auspicious time) for consecration and requested Lord Shiva's presence as well. Parshurama piled the small portion of land, consecrated the idol of Lord Anantha on it; this was the first Naga *Prathistta* (consecration of Snake God's idol) in Kerala. The place where the consecration was performed is known as Aadimoolam Vetticode.

19

LEPAKSHI: ONE TEMPLE MANY LEGENDS

During the 16th Century, there lived two brothers - Virupanna and Veeranna. Both brothers were the governors of the Vijayanagar Dynasty which was ruled by King Achutaraya. Once the King decided to build a grand temple at the place called Lepakshi and the task was given to both the brothers. Virupanna was made the treasurer by the King to take care of the money being spent to build the temple. Both brothers were skilful at work and they got onto the job with immediate effect.

Within a few months, the temple's construction was in full flow. Virupanna's popularity was gaining, and the King gave him more freedom to take financial decisions regarding the temple. Half-way through the construction of the temple, many of the other governors and courtiers of the kingdom started feeling jealous of Virupanna due to his closeness to the King, control over temple fund, and his popularity. They planned a conspiracy against Virupanna. One day, they all approached the King and complained that Virupanna was spending royal treasury money given for temple work for his own personal use. Hearing this the King became furious, he ordered to bring Virupanna to the palace and make him blind.

Virupanna was busy in Lekpakshi at the building construction site. When he came to know about the King's order, he was at the temple area where they were building Shiva Paravathy Kalyana Mandapa. It was a half-done Kalyana mandapa. On hearing the news of the King's order, Virupanna became very sad and felt hurt. To prove his innocence, Virupanna took out his own eyes with the tools used for temple construction and hurled them onto the walls of the temple. It is said that the stains of his blood from the eyes are still seen on the walls of the incomplete temple.

There are many other legends associated with Lekpashi temple - like this place is believed to be a place where bird Jatayu fell after being wounded by Ravana who had abducted Sita and was flying in his Vayu vahana. There are footprints in the temple premises which are believed to be of Sita's who stopped here for a while during her abduction by Ravana. Jatayu tried to stop Ravana and fought with him, but eventually, Ravana injured Jatayu, and he fell on the ground. When Lord Rama visited this place and found Jatayu, he said, "Le Pakshi" which means "Rise Bird" in Telugu, thus this place got its name 'Lepakshi'.

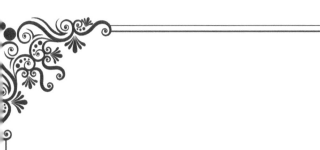

20

MAHAPRASADA

Once Narada Muni went to *Vaikuntha* (celestial abode of Vishnu) and stayed there for a few days. During his stay, he helped Goddess Laxmi very courteously. After his stay when he was about to return from Vaikuntha, Laxmi request Narada Muni to ask for any boon as she was pleased with his support during his stay. Narada Muni wished Laxmi Devi to give him the *mahaprasada* leftovers of Lord Narayana. Hearing this wish, Laxmi became gritted with anxiety as there was clear instruction from Lord Narayana that no one should be given his *prasada*. She didn't want to disobey her husband. But Narada was adamant about his wish and pleaded to Laxmi to fulfill it.

Unsure Laxmi then decided to take her chance and asked Narada Muni to wait till evening as she would try to fulfill his wish. During lunchtime, tensed Laxmi was serving food to Lord Narayana, while having his lunch Lord Narayana noticed the worried face of Laxmi. He then asked her the matter of concern. She explained the whole incident that had happened between her and Narada and requested him to help her to fulfill Narada's wish. Lord Narayana politely agreed to the request and allowed Laxmi to take his plate of remnants and give it to Narada. On hearing this, Laxmi jumped with happiness and instantly took the *mahaprasada* plate and offered it to Narada Muni.

Narada was very happy and started dancing in ecstasy for having Narayana's *mahaprasada*. He ate *mahaprasada* and started chanting Lord's name. He continued his dance and chanting. His emotion level was increasing, and he travelled many planets. Eventually, he reached Mount Kailash where Lord Shiva saw Narada dancing and chanting Lord Narayana's name. He was surprised to see Narada in this state of ecstasy. Lord Shiva asked Narada why he was so excited. He had never seen Narada this way earlier.

Narada then told that he had got a rare opportunity to have Lord Narayana's *mahaprasada* and that's the reason he was in so much pleasure and happiness. Lord Shiva was happy to hear about *mahaprasada* and asked Narada if he could also get *mahaprasada*. However, after hearing this, Narada felt sorry as he had eaten all the *prasada,* and nothing was left for others. But he was scared to say 'No' to Lord Shiva. During this time, he noticed that a morsel of *prasada* was stuck to his fingernail. Narada showed him his fingernail and told, "Yes, I have brought the *mahaprasada* for you Lord". Shiva was very happy to get a morsel of *prasada*. Narada put his finger into Shiva's mouth. As soon as the morsel of *mahaprasada* touched the tongue of Shiva, he felt great trance and cheerfulness. He started to chant and dance with ecstasy. He was feeling lucky and happy to get Narayana's *mahaprasada*. Goddess Parvati, the wife of Lord Shiva asked him the reason for his happiness. On this, Shiva told that he had received Lord Narayana's *mahaprasada* from Narada Muni. Excited Parvati asked Shiva if he had kept some *mahaprasada* for her. To this, the Lord didn't have an answer as there was none. He himself had got a small morsel from Narada's nail. Upon realising that she had been deprived of Lord Narayana's *prasada*, Parvati was angry. Furious Parvati started burning the whole universe, from the lower planets to the higher planets, the whole world felt scorching heat.

Seeing the warning situation across planets, Lord Brahma approached Narayana in *Vaikuntha* and asked his help to pacify Parvati. Narayana was kind enough to help Brahma; he reached Kailash Parbat on Garuda. When Parvati saw Narayana, she came forward and offered her obeisance. Lord Narayana told Parvati that he would give her as much *mahaprasada* she wants and requested her to give up her anger. However, Parvati requested that *mahaprasada* should be available for all humankind and living entities, without which she will not get pacified.

Lord Narayana agreed to her wish and said that her wish would be fulfilled once he appears in Nilachaladham, where his temple will be famous for distributing *mahaprasada*. All of his *prasada* will be offered to Parvati first, only after that, the remnants will become *mahaprasada*. Devotees who will consume his *prasada* will be liberated. *Mahaprasada* will get distributed to everyone without contemplation. Parvati Devi's temple will be built next to Lord Narayana's temple in the courtyard. As Lord Shiva had neglected to offer *mahaprasada* to Parvati, his temple will be at some distance outside the courtyard.

All this appeared to be true as Lord Narayana appeared in Puri as Jagannath and Parvati Devi as Bimala. All of Jagannath's *prasada* is offered first to Bimala Devi, after which it's distributed as *mahaprasada*. There is no difference made between low and high-caste for taking Jagannath's *mahaprasada*.

21

WHEN HANUMAN
TURNED RED

Once Lord Rama and Sita returned to Ayodhya from Lanka, Hanuman also stayed back in the palace as he always wanted to serve Lord Rama. Hanuman accompanied Rama everywhere. One day when Devi Sita entered Lord Rama's bedroom for sleep, Hanuman also followed her. Seeing this, Lord Rama told Hanuman that he could not enter the room. Surprised Hanuman asked Rama, "If Sita Devi can enter your bedroom then why can't I?" Seeing such innocent devotion and to convince Hanuman, Lord Rama told him that as Devi Sita has *sindoor* (Vermilion) on her forehead, that's why she can enter his bedroom.

Hanuman came out, and the whole night kept thinking about the incident and concluded that *sindoor* is the prerequisite to enter Lord Rama's bedroom. The next day, he went to Devi Sita and asked the real purpose of *sindoor*. Sita knew what Hanuman wanted. She explained that she puts *sindoor* on her forehead to lengthen the lifespan of Rama. Hanuman, after hearing this, understood the secret of *sindoor*.

Without wasting much time, he rushed to the market to get *sindoor*. He reached one shop where he asked the shopkeeper to give him *sindoor*. The shopkeeper handed over one small box of *sindoor* to him. Seeing the small amount of *sindoor*, Hanuman got disappointed. He just went into the shop, opened all the bags of *sindoor* and emptied it all over his body. He poured some *sindoor* on the floor and trolled over to cover his entire body with it. He then walked back to the palace.

Once he reached the palace, he went and met Lord Rama. After seeing Hanuman in red color, surprised

Ram enquired. Sita also came there, and when she saw Hanuman full of *sindoor* and his entire body in red color, she started laughing and informed Ram that she had told Hanuman that *sindoor* would increase the life of his *Prabhu* Rama.

Actually, Hanuman thought if a small amount of *sindoor* on Sita's forehead can increase the lifespan of Rama, then if he put *sindoor* all over his body, it can make Rama eternal. That's how unadulterated love Hanuman had for Rama. Since then Hanuman's red idol is worshipped in many temples.

22

CONFRONTATION
FOR AMRIT

Sage Kashyap had many wives, and among them Vinata and Kadru were sisters. Sage Kashyap gave a boon to both the sisters to have choices for giving birth to their children. As per their wishes, Kadru became the mother of 1000 snakes (Nagas) and Vinata laid two eggs in the desire of getting two sons. Both eggs had not hatched for a very long time. One day, Vinata decided to break one egg to see if all was well. However, once she broke the egg, she was shocked to see the child inside the egg, which was not completely formed. The child cursed her to become a slave of someone and suffer the rest of her life like a servant. Vinata feared this curse, so she asked for forgiveness. After seeing his mother in this condition, the child told her that if she be patient with the other egg and allow his brother to come out of it in its own time then his brother would save her. Later Vinata's first child, Aruna, became a charioteer and a messenger for the sun god.

A few months after this incident, Kadru and Vinata had a bet, where Kadru challenged Vinata to guess the color of the tail of Uchchaihshravas, the divine white horse which is a vehicle of the Sun God with seven heads. Everyone knew that Uchchaihshravas is a white horse and Vinata's answer was obvious that the tail of Uchchaihshravas is white. However, Kadru had a different plan; she tricked Vinata by directing her sons (snakes) to curl around the horse's tail, which made the tail appear black. This way Vinata lost the bet; thus she became the slave of Kadru and her snake sons.

During this phase of Vinata's life, the second egg hatched, and her second child came out of it. This child was special with the body of a human but the face with a beak, wings and claws of an eagle. As soon as he was born, he was a slave of Kadru and her snake sons as his mother was a slave to them. The child's name was Garuda. When he was growing, he was not happy and very angry with the way her mother was getting treated like a servant. One day, Garuda asked his mother why only she did all the household work and how she became a slave of Kadru and her sons. To this, Vinata narrated the entire incident of the bet between her and Kadru. After hearing the story, he felt more anger and wanted to teach a lesson to his snake brothers.

He went to the snakes and asked what they would need to grant freedom to him and his mother from their slavery. He was clear in his thought. The snakes were clever, and they knew Garuda was enormously powerful, both physically and mentally. He could achieve any task if he set it in his mind. After a long discussion among themselves, the snakes asked Garuda to get them *amrit,* the nectar of the Devas, which they had got from "*Samundra Manthan*", churning of the ocean. Devas had denied *amrit* to *Asuras*.

Anyone who drank *amrit* became powerful and strong, hence the snakes thought if they get access to *amrit,* they could become immortal with more power than others. The snakes knew that it's only Garuda who could get them *amrit* from Devas. Garuda was prepared for this challenge, and his aim was to release his mother from slavery. He took his mother's blessings and started his journey to get the *amrit.*

Very soon, Devas came to know about Garuda's plan and his intentions to get the *amrit*. It was a worrying environment in heaven. Brihaspati, Vedic sage who counselled the gods, informed Lord Indira about Garuda's plan. Indira turned pale with fear as he knew how powerful Garuda is. Come what may, Indira could not let the *amrit* go to the snakes. Indira called for an emergency meeting with all the Gods to discuss how to deal with Garuda's attack and save *amrit* from him. During the meeting, all the Gods decided to go for a full-fledged war against Garuda and crush him to death.

Eventually, the war started between Garuda and Devas. Within no time Devas realised that Garuda is massive and surely, they would lose the war and *amrit* to Garuda. Devas' fear turned into reality, Garuda fought courageously with all the Devas. He reached near the *amrit* pot and got hold of it and flew away. Once he got hold of the pot, he grew himself bigger in size and with happiness he flew in the sky. He was happy because now his mother would be free from Kadru and the snakes.

Lord Vishnu was seeing this incident and was amazed to see how brave Garuda was, and even after getting *amrit* in his custody, he never thought of taking *amrit* for himself. Before Garuda could reach Kadru's place, Lord Vishnu stopped Garuda and said, "Garuda, I am impressed by your character and braveness. I am happy to see how you fought the war ethically with Devas and took *amrit* in your custody. I grant you any boon of your choice, please tell me what you want?"

Seeing Lord Vishnu, Garuda felt a surge of devotion and with folded hands, bowed his head and said, "Hey

Lord Vishnu, my first wish is to become immortal without drinking *amrit*." Lord Vishnu blessed him and said, "Tatashthu."

Blessed Garuda then told Lord Vishnu that he is overwhelmed with his gesture and wants to give whatever Lord Vishnu wants. To which Lord Vishnu said, "I want you to be my vehicle and carry me around the world." Garuda at once agreed for the same; however he had another job to finish first before becoming a vehicle of Lord Vishnu. He must give the *amrit* pot to the snakes and free himself and his mother from them. He sought Lord Vishnu's blessings and flew.

When Garuda was about to reach Kadru's place, Indira came back to fight and challenged him. Garuda fought with Indira and defeated him. Indira was now helpless, and he knew that getting into a war with Garuda would not serve his purpose of getting the *amrit* pot back. Indira then bowed down to Garuda and requested if he can take the *amrit* pot back as soon as Garuda gives it to the snakes. This way he could free his mother and the snakes would not become immortal. Garuda liked the idea and agreed to execute the plan. Indira was very happy now and asked Garuda to ask any wish, and he would grant the same. Garuda thought that all issues started because his snake brothers mistreated him and his mother. He wanted to teach a lesson to the snakes. Hence, he asked Indira to make snakes his natural food. Indira granted this wish to Garuda.

After this, Garuda reached home and gave the *amrit* pot to the snakes. The snakes were overjoyed, and they turned to Garuda and his mother Vinata and said, "You both are free now, and you are not our servants anymore." Garuda and Vinata were very happy and started leaving the place. During this time Garuda turned back and told the snakes, "You have the *amrit* pot with you now, you will be immortal shortly. It would be better if you all take a bath before tasting *amrit*." The snakes agreed to Garuda's suggestion and kept the pot of *amrit* on sharp grass called '*Kusha*' and went to the river to take a bath. As soon as the snakes got into the river, Indira came and took away the pot. Both Garuda and Vinata were watching this from far away with smiles on their faces.

The snakes came out of the river and found the pot missing, and they saw Indira taking away the *amrit*. Few of the drops fell on sharp '*Kusha*' grass. The snakes thought to get at least a few drops of *amrit* from the grass blades. However, due to the sharp edges of the grass, the snakes' tongues got cut. It is believed that since then snakes have split tongue.

Garuda was happy to have taken revenge from the snakes and for freeing his mother from slavery. Later, he went to *Vaikuntha* (the celestial abode of Vishnu) and became the vehicle of Lord Vishnu.

Made in United States
Troutdale, OR
04/14/2024

19185378R00070